BHANTE

The Corgi of O'side

written by

DEBORAH BURGGRAAF

photography by

CHUCK FASILIS

PROTECTIVE HANDS
Communications

ISBN: 978-1-7349267-0-5

Library of Congress Catalog Control Number: 2020916616

Published by
Protective Hands Communications
Riviera Beach, FL 33404
Phone: 561-841-4990
www.protectivehands.com
Email: info@protectivehands.com

Printed in the United States of America

For Sharon Gibson and Chuck Fasilis,
thank you for sharing Bhante with me and teaching me loving kindness.

As the foggy morning rolled in slowly, the gray blanketed our Pacific Coast.
Bhante, my wide-eyed Corgi, stood with his perked ears, waiting patiently with hope.

After gathering Bhante's chewies along with his leash,
I placed the cell phone in my pocket, smiling, "Let's not forget your treats!"

Bhante's begging eyes were calling, "Are you ready, yet? "Can we go now, pretty please?"

Wearing his 'Service Dog' vest adorned by the lead of his leash,
we closed our front door and remembered our keys.

Down the cement steps we walked and were welcomed to see,
the Pacific Ocean dancing beyond the Torrey Pine trees.

Out on the *Oceanside Pier*, we now became part of the Pacific coast vibe.
People are walking and talking, as surfers slide into black skins, so tight.

Life is alive and we are, too!

Captured by the crisp, morning fog,
we strolled through the cool mist, watching the runners jog.

"Oh, your puppy is so cute! Can I pet him, oh, please?"
Bhante stops with his pause, smiling back with glee.

We carry on our walk along the wooden planked *O'side Pier,* as
fishermen cast their lines next to water buckets and their gear.

"It's a Corgi! It's a Corgi!" We hear wherever we go.
Deep in the golden sand, Bhante plays like he's in fallen snow!

Though his legs are so short and his eyes like chocolate drops,
his sharp ears are so keen, even when we pause to make a stop.

We walk and we walk, my star Corgi, with zest!
As we wander, Bhante gives back only his very best!

He struts and he stops, and Bhante wants to see more,
even the brightly, blooming roses and the flowers next door.

We stroll along Coast Highway, as Bhante sniffs every section of grass.
He confidently walks past Mr. Crow, who turns his head real fast.

At the base of the parking meter, Bhante's pee-pee is his marked spot.
"Over there? What about here?" He glances around, "Please, can we stop?"

Downtown along the walkway, we absorb the scenic scape of the coastal surf.
It's time for a quick poopie break—Bhante marks his own turf.

The locals and the tourists love Bhante's grand smile.
Often, they stop and visit for quite a while.

Bhante is full of discovery; he is the lead on *Pier View Way*.
When families joyfully walk over, they sit down and stay!

Around the block at the pizza shop, Bhante sniffs hoping for a nibble,
of a pie crumb or pepperoni that someone happens to dribble.

At the street market every Thursday, Bhante loves to explore
jewelry and fashion, and the exotic tastes from next door.

While I search through displays of stylish clothes, pausing at the shoes,
Bhante patiently sits by my feet—his love is so true.

Hungry after shopping, we stop at the taco shop for a plate of beef taquitos, with black beans with rice, and zesty tomatoes.

My Bhante, my buddy, my love at the Pacific Coast.
"Are you ready to head to the harbor now? Let's carry on with high hopes!"

We made our way over to the quaint *O'side Harbor*,
as we popped in and said hello to the local barber!

The white boats gently rocked across the settled, salty bay,
as the locals welcomed tourists on this coastal, afternoon day.

At the picnic tables we sit, with our burgers and fries,
watching the lazy, rolling blue tide.

Wherever Bhante goes, making new friends is fun!
But for this Corgi in 'Service,' his mission is never done.

"Sit. Stay. Okay!" are all commands that Bhante owns.
If the time were needed, he would assist without even a, *"No!"*

With each command given, Bhante is ready to gladly help,
with a jump, or a run, or even his mighty, *"Yelp!"*

As the west coast slowly drops her sunset in disguise,
Bhante and I sit watching the orange ball disappear with wide eyes.

Under our cozy blanket snuggling at the shore,
we end our fun day together, only wanting more.

As we turn to walk home, we slowly head to the right,
pausing to reminisce over our glorious, Pacific sights!

Bhante, the *Pembroke Welsh Corgi* known in this O'side town,
confident, yet curious—you're always the STAR of the crowd!

Now almost back, we climb up a few stairs.
"One more treat," Bhante pauses, with his cute little Corgi glare.

Our front door opens and Bhante is happy to be back home.
He quickly laps his fresh water from his blue, heart bowl.

Resting in the living room with your treats, I wipe your chocolate eyes.
The night crawls in with the stars sparkling across the coastal sky.

Tucked in bed with your bunny toy, you cozy in for the night,
ready to dream about all the Oceanside sights.

Dreaming about the fisherman with the crowds and crows that sing,
with shopping and food treats, fit only for a royal king!

Glancing up at me, you beg for one more walkie, *"Please?"*
Your eyes slowly close and you fall into your deep sleep.

Bhante, The Corgi of O'side, now lost in his sleep,
dreaming of all the downtown delights, with even one more treat!

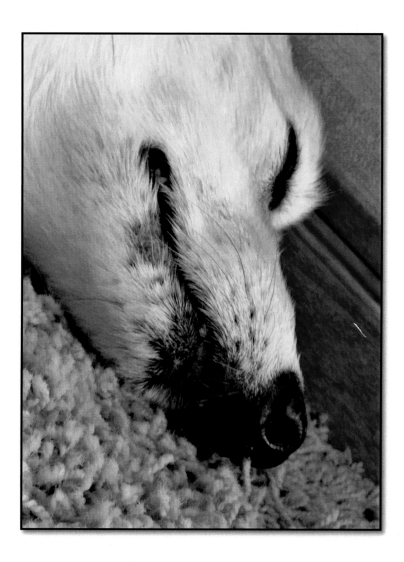

The O'side Pier, the delicious food, and the shopping we did,
now swirl around in his dozy, little head.

The daily joy and love that Bhante gives to all he meets,
with his tender, *'Hello,'* and caring eyes, are always ready to greet.

Bhante walks along the shoreline as the waves settle down.
He stops for a moment and welcomes a new friend to his town.

Dreaming about my mom and dad, we always treasure our daily walks,
filled with loving kindness that we give away to all.

While on the *O'side Pier*, we glance up to see,
the seagulls and Pelicans and the deep, blue Pacific Ocean rippling by me.

"It's a Corgi! It's a Corgi!" They excitedly call.
Bhante struts, turns his head, and stands so proud and so tall.

THE END

Please scan the QR code above to access *"Bhante's video"* by Chuck Fasilis

Afterword

We feel so blessed and grateful of having the privilege of rescuing our amazing dog, Bhante, *a Welsh Corgi*.

In 2006 when he was only three years old, we found Bhante in Rancho Mirage, California at a rescue center. At first he was shy, until he discovered the wonderful, golf fairway in the back of our home where he could chase tennis balls to his heart's content. The fairway became the 'meeting place' for all his other doggie friends.

This was Bhante's passion for many years, along with long walks, adventures with us driving to Canada, riding ferries, exploring Big Sur, and walking in four, 5K Fundraising events to raise money for the *Diabetes and Heart Associations*.

In 2016, we moved to Oceanside, California where Bhante enjoyed long walks out to the harbor, the *Oceanside Pier* and of course, running on the beach. Wherever we went, people shouted, *"Corgi! Corgi!"* Everyone always wanted to pet him.

Bhante was so adorable, and so smart and loved the attention. We trained him as a *Service Dog* to meet our needs, which also allowed him to visit restaurants, attend the theatre and enjoy museums. Bhante was the love of our lives for nearly fourteen years.

by Sharon Gibson and Chuck Fasilis

About the Author

Deborah Burggraaf is a retired middle school teacher of over twenty years. Ms. Burggraaf continues to educate, inspire, and dedicate her life to our youth, with readings, school visits, library presentations and virtual book shares on her ***Facebook Page and YouTube Channel***--**Deborah Burggraaf Books**

Ms. Burggraaf has received ten *Florida Authors and Publishers Association Book Awards* for her children's books and in 2020, she was named a finalist by the International Book Awards for her children's book, *Josie on Shadowridge Drive*. Ms. Burggraaf has been recognized as a, *"prolific writer of children's books,"* of the twenty-first century. Ms. Burggraaf's books are available at: www.dburgg.com and www.amazon.com.

About the Photographer

Chuck Fasilis has been involved in all facets of corporate video production. Mr. Fasilis is now focusing on areas of imaging, education, travel, and entertainment. You can view Chuck's YouTube videos highlighting, *Corgi of O'side*, where you will fall in love with Bhante sharing his autobiography of his fun-filled life: https://youtu.be/XhYyP_HZM10

Author Deborah Burggraaf & Bhante

Oceanside, California

<u>Other Books by Deborah Burggraaf</u>

Caught in the Middle

Cooka, The Bird without Wings

Boonie-Freedom Runner

Crow No More

Hot Wheels for Benny

At the Pig Races

Flutternutter-The Dance of the Zebra Butterfly

The Noodle Club

Resilient Red

Sasha's Birthday Party

The Lovebug Connection

BLUE-Night Crawlers

Josie on Shadowridge Drive

Corky's Travels

MISS DEACON and The Tale of William